D1244457

COLLECTING EAMES
THE JF CHEN COLLECTION

I am extremely grateful for the chance to share a few words about the JF Chen Eames Collection in these pages. Most people who explore the work of Charles and Ray Eames soon come to learn that, as beautiful as the objects are, the ideas behind them are just as beautiful. And no concept was more critical than the notion of the Guest/Host relationship—Charles said that the role of the designer was essentially that of a good host, anticipating the needs of the guest.

Now, most of the key Eames furniture collections (Vitra Design Museum, primus inter pares, as well as MOMA, The Henry Ford and the Eames Family collection) are focused on the development of the furniture through the Eameses' iterative design process. In other words: the treasured prototypes and experiments. This is, of course, an essential aspect of being a good host, to work out the ideas and bring a beautiful and appropriate chair into production—but it is just the beginning of the story. Remember: the chair that the Eameses were designing was not simply the vintage piece—however magical; the chair they were designing is the authentic chair that will be made tomorrow. The JF Chen Eames Collection is the first collection of any scale devoted to exploring and understanding the second part of that story—the constant improvement of each product long after it went into production. This too is part of being a good host and, as such, vitally important to Charles and Ray Eames.

As Dick Donges, who worked at the Eames Office, once told me, an Eames chair design—was never finished—even after it started to be manufactured. This is because Charles and Ray devoted a significant amount of their personal time and Eames Office resources to working with Herman Miller and Vitra to be sure the designs were not only made right, but continued to be improved throughout their lifetime of service. They wanted every chair, not simply the first ones, to be wonderful—and preferably more wonderful than the one before it. (The transition from X-base to H-base is but one example captured in these pieces.)

The quality and breadth of the collection is a tribute to two men. Daniel Ostroff, the scholar and collector who collected the first 150 chairs, and Joel Chen who has expanded it to over 400 pieces. And here I need to thank Joel on behalf of our family for something as unique as the collection itself. Knowing the special nature of this collection and because of Dan's scholarship particularly in terms of helping people understand the ideas behind the furniture, Joel did something quite generous. He paid for high quality photographs to be taken of the chairs in a consistent format and provided those for the new website, eamesdesigns.com, a virtual encyclopedia of all things Eames.

More than a few of the chairs you see here may well be considered the archetypal example of their era of manufacture.

—Eames Demetrios, *September 4, 2011*

The JF Chen Eames Collection is unparalleled in its importance to scholars and to collectors. It is the only collection that brings together so many great Eames designs, from every decade of Eames design production. In this introduction, I will highlight some specific items and certain standout aspects of the collection. But without a doubt, the most important aspect of The JF Chen Eames Collection is its entirety. Every individual piece in this collection tells a part of one story, the story of the acclaimed designers, Charles and Ray Eames.

Collectors and dealers have often contributed significantly to the history of twentieth century design—by rescuing and preserving pieces for future study, by studying them in detail, by allowing others to study them, and by sharing what they see and learn. JF Chen is a family business and together, Joel, Margaret, Bianca, and Fiona Chen think of their collection—now over 400 pieces, as a resource not only for specialists, but also for anyone who wants to know more about the work of Charles and Ray Eames.

The JF Chen Eames Collection began with my own collection. I started collecting Eames and other post-war designs in 1987, but eventually, as happens to many who focus on post-war designs, as I became a more experienced collector, I became a focused Eames collector. By the time JF Chen bought my Eames collection, it had grown to 175 pieces.

As JF Chen expanded the collection from 175 to 425 pieces, nothing went into the collection unless I wanted to study it, and unless Joel liked it. Joel has impeccable taste and the fact that he buys only those things that he likes, distinguishes him from others, and makes him more of a collector than most antique dealers. As Joel often says, "I don't know who will buy what, so I buy what I like."

I want to underscore the Chen's generous acceptance of the requests that I attached to our work on this collection. I was to have free access to all of the pieces for study and documentation and for as long as it took, which meant that JF Chen would sell none in the meantime. I was allowed to choose the photographer and to direct an exhaustive photographic campaign, documenting every piece from every angle with many close-ups. This documentary photography, which involved many weeks of work on the part of professional photographer Grant Taylor, who at one time worked for the Eames Office.

Together we decided to grow this collection according to certain principles, and these principles were informed by the way that Charles and Ray Eames designed the pieces. We collected the best examples from every decade of Eames designs and we did this because Charles and Ray Eames continuously worked to improve their designs. This becomes clear when one looks at this collection.

George Nelson, Herman Miller's legendary director of design, repeatedly attested to how Charles and Ray Eames constantly worked to improve their designs. He said they fussed over them like they were their children. One of several ways this collection illustrates their dedication to improvement is by the inclusion of Eames Storage Units. George Nelson wrote about the ESUs', "…these first units developed some 'bugs' when put into use, and also, when completing the group, the designers found they had a number of new ideas worth incorporating." In the words of Charles and Ray, who designed and wrote the words for the brochure heralding the Second Series of the ESUs, "this new [Second] edition of Eames Storage Units has been improved and refined so as to give greater service and pleasure to the customer." For this collection, we focused on these Second Series ESUs, but there is also the rare brochure for and examples of, the First Edition, notably two rare desks.

The earliest piece in the collection is a 1939 Kleinhans chair by Charles Eames and Eero Saarinen made for the Kleinhans Music Hall in Buffalo, New York. In this collection you can see how that relates to a later Eames design, the 1958 Eames aluminum group chair. Another value of this collection is in seeing how the designs evolved as Charles and Ray Eames became more experienced. They always said that their practice followed the example of history—good work is done when one builds on what has gone on before.

The next earliest piece is a unique, most likely the only complete (with its original upholstery) privately owned example of the high back chair from the 1941 Organic Design competition at MOMA, won by Charles Eames and Eero Saarinen. That's the chair that changed everything when it came to furniture

design. It also marked the first occasion on which Charles collaborated with Ray Kaiser, who would later become his wife. The last chair in the collection is an authentic Eames La Chaise, authorized and licensed by Ray Eames and the Eames family, and first manufactured in 1996.

In between, one will find great designs from the 1940s, '50s, '60s, '70s, and '80s. The JF Chen Eames Collection has plenty of the pieces that some new collectors focus on— the earliest molded plywood chairs and the earliest molded plastic chairs. But its significance to collectors and scholars is that it has much, much more.

Some collectors look for Eames "prototypes." Charles and Ray Eames designed by making life-size three-dimensional models in their own studio although I do not believe they made prototypes of the sort made by other designers. There are Eames models in The Chen Collection, including a very precious one—a pre-production Eames aluminum group dining table with an onyx top. Any stone top Eames table is a rarity, and because The JF Chen Collection includes other aluminum group tables with stone tops (production examples) we can see that the production tables are superior to this model, which needs to be used delicately, if at all. By comparing and contrasting the model with the production examples, we can see what Charles and Ray learned from modeling. The production examples are more beautiful and show much more design care, and thought. They are not delicate, and

I believe that in normal use, they will last a long time.

In reference to models, I will share something about an exhibition I saw at LACMA in 2007, featuring a Picasso lithograph, "Minotaurmachy." Somehow they located and exhibited various early versions (models) of the finished lithograph that marked a big technological and artistic breakthrough for Picasso. It was an interesting aspect of the exhibit to see the various versions made by Picasso, the ones he made as he worked through the problem. But I am sure that I was not the only visitor to walk away thinking, "Yeah, but the best one in the show was the finished lithograph, made in concert with his lithographers, that one is the best! That one is the authentic Picasso." And that final version is the one that Picasso ultimately offered to the art collectors. I believe the best authentic Eames designs are the ones manufactured for and used by the Eames customers.

Charles and Ray Eames licensed the production of their designs to specific manufacturers and supervised their production. It may be useful to compare this with the practice of a great sculptor, Auguste Rodin. Many authentic Rodin pieces were cast both before and after his death. He knew and approved of the outfit that made them, and he did not place any limit on how many should be made. (The idea of a "limited edition" is relatively recent in the fine arts.) In the same way one could order an authentic Rodin bronze, in some cases, a licensed Eames manufacturer may produce as many examples of an Eames piece as the public will order. Charles and Ray passed along to their heirs the responsibility of supervising production.

However, Charles and Ray Eames did not create designs to be put on pedestals. They worked as hard as they did, to paraphrase Charles and Ray, so that great pieces could be used and enjoyed by the most number of people. Relating to this, The JF Chen Eames Collection has a number of sets of chairs and tables. They are not only great historic examples, but one can use them in the way they were intended. One can see a rare matched set of six rosewood DCMS from the 1960s, a great set of four DKR-1s, with contrasting upholstery, many pairs, and still more sets of four chairs, eight chairs and pairs, that you can match to authentic, vintage tables. There are sets of chairs with their original tables as well. It is extraordinary, with rare Eames pieces, to have as many sets as are in this collection.

One person who knew Charles and Ray Eames well said, "There is no Eames style, there's a legacy of problems beautifully solved." This means that organizing this catalog presented a special challenge. Finally, we decided to organize it, to some degree, by the materials used even though Charles and Ray were not "material" driven designers. They were focused on the product and its service and performance for the customer. However, over the years, their authorized manufacturers have classified Eames designs by material, so this catalog does that as well.

I will conclude with three comments about how we put this collection together, each relating to how Charles and Ray Eames worked. First, we focused as much as possible on Eames designs that were complete in all details. The Eames molded plastic chairs in this collection are example of this. One can see, various chairs with various glides, and this was not an arbitrary design decision. There was intention on the part of Charles and Ray Eames, as they always thought about the entire design, every part.

One of the many things we can learn from this collection is that between1950 and 1957, as a result of Charles and Ray's attention to detail, the glides on The Eames Chair changed four times. The fourth and final glide is the white nylon glide, and it is virtually indestructible in normal use. Herman Miller employees have attested to Charles and Ray's personal attention to chair glides. For this collection we looked for Eames designs with original screws because the designers of these chairs cared about such things. As Charles and Ray Eames wrote, "The details are not details—the make the product…the gauge of the wire, the selection of the wood, the finish of the castings."

An excerpt from a 1977 interview with Stan Schrotenboer, then a Herman Miller general foreman, exemplifies this point. "Charles used to come about twice a year through the areas where we were manufacturing not only his designs but other designs. We have run into occasions when Charles has said that some-thing did not have the class, or the feel, of his design and of Herman Miller. He said once that a screw in a chair may sound like a little thing, but the screw has to be the right design and the right color—maybe it isn't visible, but it's part of the product, and it still shows that what you put in a chair speaks of Charles Eames and Herman Miller."

Next, we focused almost entirely on Herman Miller examples because it was with Herman Miller that Charles and Ray first reached a national market and eventually, an international market, for their designs. Within less than six months of the Eames designs debuting at the Museum of Modern Art in New York City in 1946, Herman Miller was on board. The one Vitra chair is the beautiful Eames La Chaise, manufactured for the very first time in 1996, and according to Charles and Ray Eames' exacting specifications. My future scholarship will include a detailed study of the Vitra examples, and examples by all of the other authorized manufacturers over the years.

Finally, Charles and Ray Eames did not brand their authentic goods. They did not think folks would appreciate buying something and having someone else's name and logo burnished too visibly on to it. That means that a collection like this has added importance, because every piece in this collection has been carefully studied with regard to authenticity, but more importantly, each piece comes with a guarantee from JF Chen, an establishment with a 37-year history and reputation, and with many repeat customers.

I will conclude by dedicating this book and collection to two families who do so much for design scholarship, and for the cause of good design. The Eames family comprises the daughter, Lucia Eames, and the grandchildren of Charles and Ray Eames—Byron Atwood, Lucia Eames, Eames Demetrios, Llisa Demetrios, and Carla Hartman. And the Chen family members are Joel and Margaret Chen, and their daughters Fiona and Bianca. The members of the Eames family are the principals of the Eames Office and the Eames Foundation. Joel, Margaret, Bianca and Fiona together comprise the business known as JF Chen.

The Eames family, by inviting me to contribute to their website, gave me a platform and an opportunity. Above all else, they gave me a place to learn, to conduct research, and a place to present it. They funded the architecture of a new site, eamesdesigns.com, a virtual encyclopedia of all things Eames, and I am the editor.

The Chens are some of the nicest and most generous people one could ever hope to meet. They not only bought my original collection, but they were very patient with me and worked together to realize a complex project. At eamesdesigns.com, their generosity can be seen through some of the extraordinary documentation projects that they supported. It is truly a lasting legacy. The Chens provided me with the resources to study the collection the way Charles and Ray Eames recommended studying anything—through the lens of a camera. It was said that Charles felt one could

not understand a design unless one photographed it, and I feel that one can seldom go wrong by following his example.

The Eames family continues the legacy of Charles and Ray Eames by supervising all of the current production of authentic Eames designs. The grandchildren are Lucia Eames' legacy to the world, and they work very hard to make sure that great and authentic Eames products continue to be made every day.

The Chens supervised the design and development of this book, and they are overseeing this amazing exhibition. Bianca has a great eye, and a very good understanding of Eames designs. When I showed her a contemporary "skate-board school" graphic that might be used for this exhibition she demurred, and said this exhibition should be done in the classic and timeless manner that characterized Eames work. Fiona is a serious student of art and therefore is a serious contributor to everything you see at JF Chen.

Margaret Chen and Lucia Eames are the rocks and foundations of both families.

—Daniel Ostroff

EAMES
SAARINEN

"The most advanced of all these systems appears in a group of chairs by Saarinen and Eames. In an ordinary chair there are a seat and a back which support the body at two or three points. In the case of a usual large upholstered chair the body sinks into a general softness until it reaches support. The principle in these chairs is that of continuous contact and support, with a thin rubber pad for softness at all points. The shell is formed of strips of veneer and glue laminated in a cast-iron form developed by the Haskelite Corporation. In this way more comfortable support is secured with a minimum of material."

From the book, *Organic Design*, published by the Museum of Modern Art, NY, 1941.

"Revolutionary Body-Moulding Chair by Saarinen & Eames. Entirely new way legs are attached, gives resiliency never before obtained."

From the brochure, *BLOOMINGDALE'S PRESENTS ORGANIC DESIGN Furniture and Furnishings Planned for Today's Living*, sponsored by The Museum of Modern Art, published in 1941.

"The case furniture designed by Saarinen and Eames is veneered in Honduras mahogany. It carries the principle of standardization farther than any other group yet produced in this country. An 18 inch module was adopted, the units being 18 inches square (or 36 inches in length for the dining room cases). The bases on which these units rest are 13 inches high and come in lengths to hold two, three or four units, and may be used in combination to make larger groupings as well."

From the book, *Organic Design*, published by the Museum of Modern Art, NY, 1941.

"Living room group by Saarinen & Eames. Literally millions of variations possible. Basic benches, Honduras mahogany veneer on poplar."

From the brochure, *BLOOMINGDALE'S PRESENTS ORGANIC DESIGN Furniture and Furnishings Planned for Today's Living*, sponsored by The Museum of Modern Art, published in 1941.

MOLDED PLYWOOD

"The most comfortable chairs you have ever sat in. The most practical furniture you have ever owned.

Charles Eames, the designer, and Evans Products Co., the manufacturer, have made use of today's most original design thinking and advanced techno-logical processes to bring you chairs designed to fit your body and to yield to it; chairs and tables that are light to lift or carry: furniture with permanently/finished surfaces easier to keep clean than any furniture you have ever had.

Because the furniture, with its revolutionary construction, can be mass-produced by methods hitherto unheard-of, it reaches you at prices you can afford.

Beauty is inherent in the sculpted curves, the fine wood textures and colors, the clean details that endow the furniture with a look of lightness and grace.

The collection includes: dining tables, dining chairs, lounge chairs, occasional tables and a screen."

From a 1946 brochure, *The Collection of Molded Plywood Furniture*, created by the Eames Office.

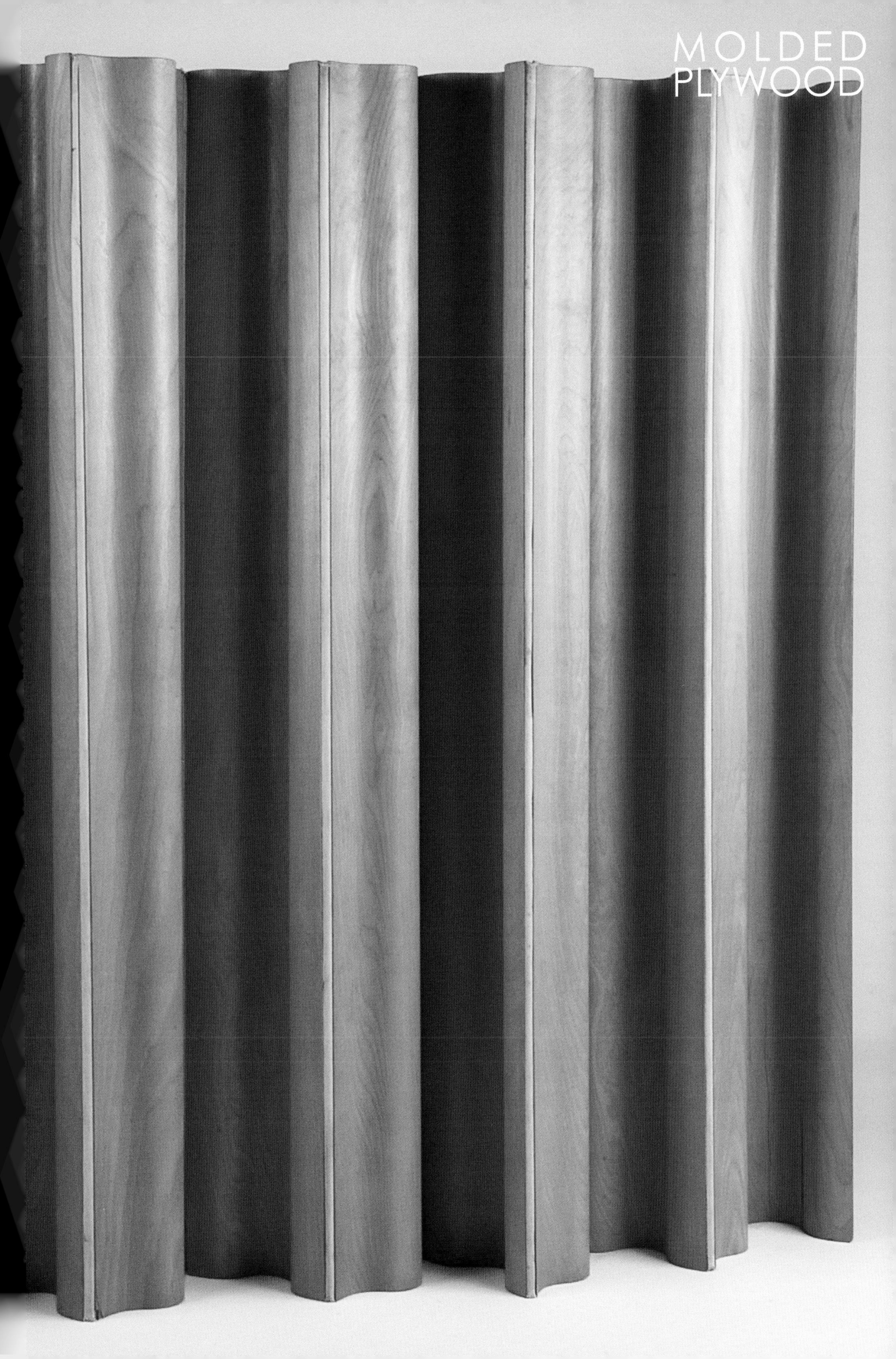

MOLDED PLYWOOD

36

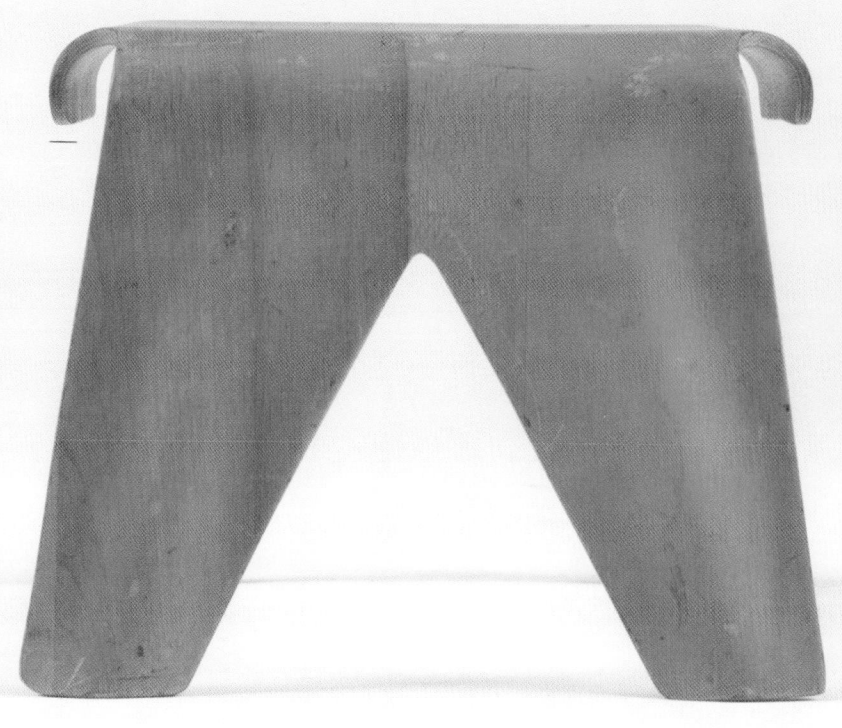

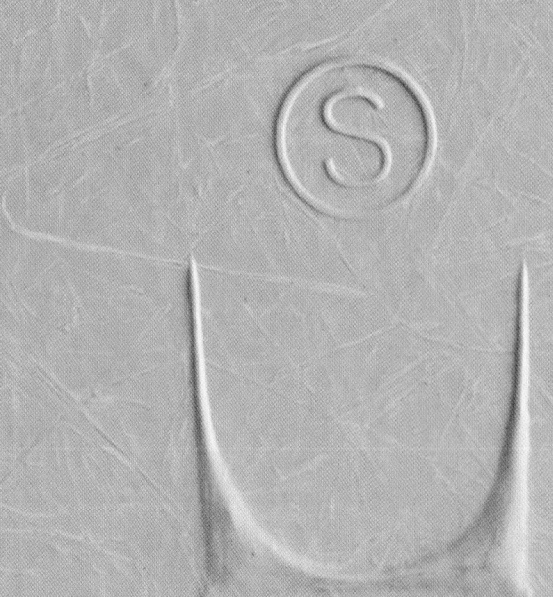

HERMAN MILLER

MOLDED PLASTIC

"A fitting companion to the famous molded plywood chairs...are these new arm chairs of molded plastic...that is pleasant to the touch, light, and will withstand stains and is virtually indestructible.

The plastic shell was skillfully molded to provide exceptional comfort.

These new arm chairs were among the prize winners in the Low Cost Furniture Competition conducted by the Museum of Modern Art.

By means of large production schedules, this chair is offered at prices that make it a genuine achievement in attractive, durable seating."
From a 1950 brochure, *Plastic Chairs by Charles Eames*, created by the Eames Office.

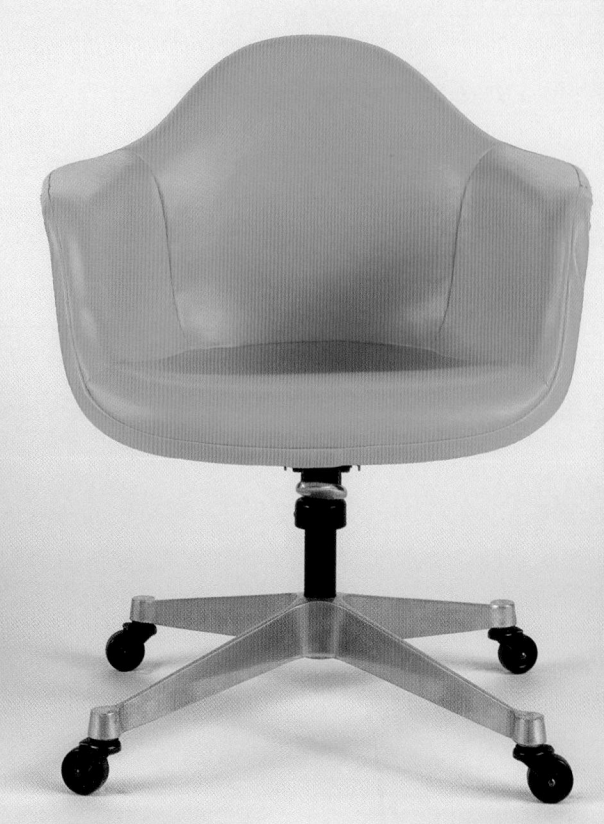

46

47

48

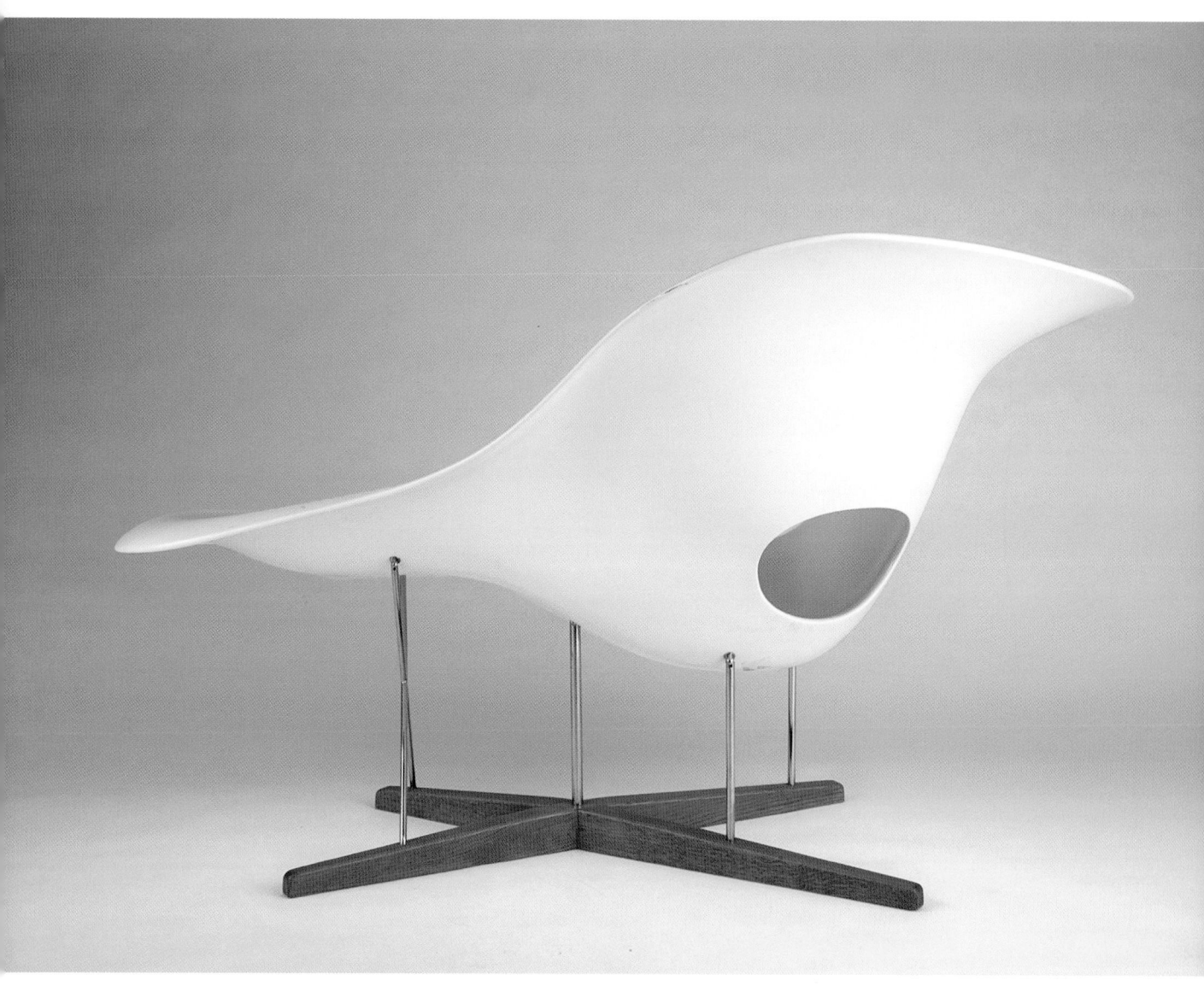

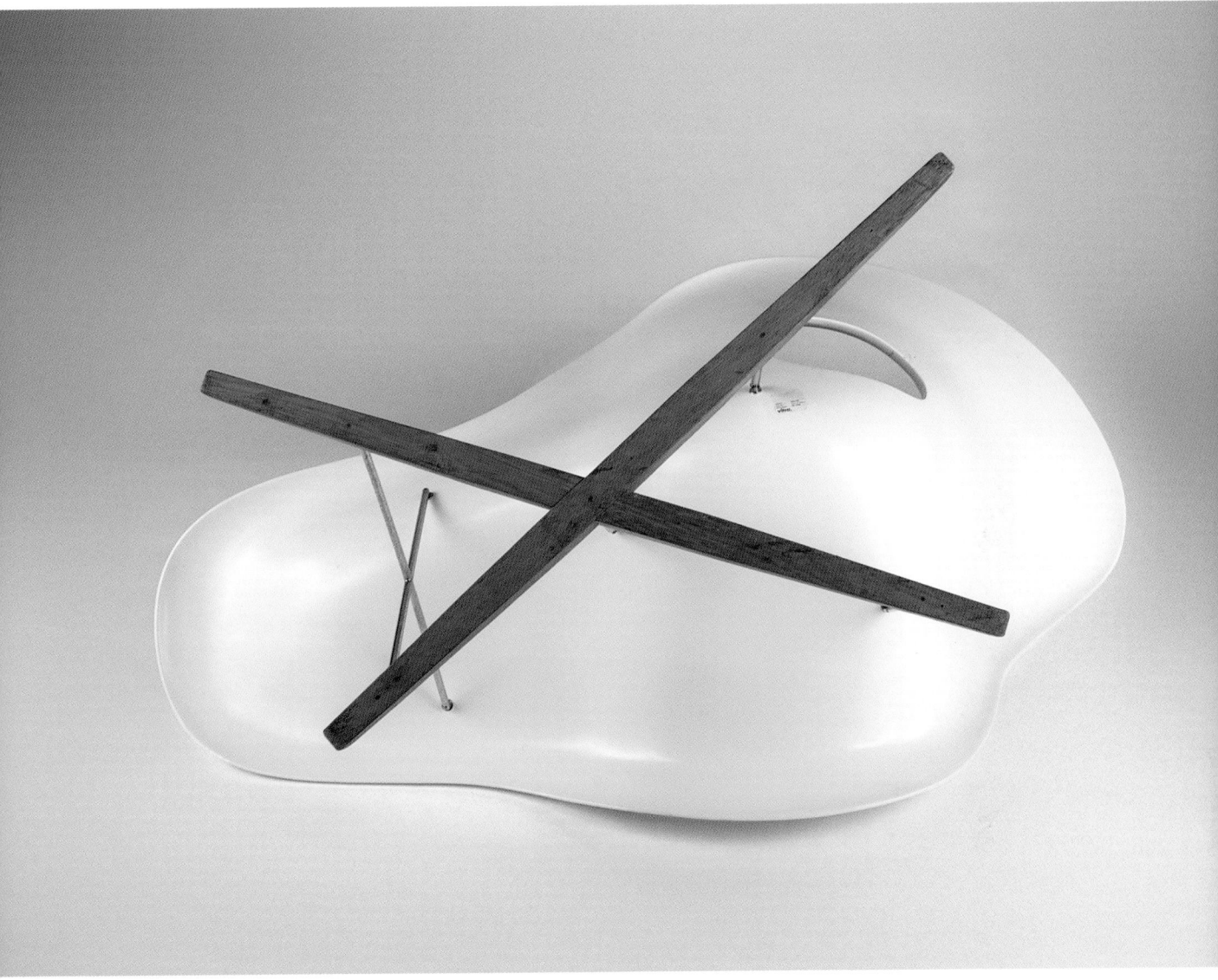

64

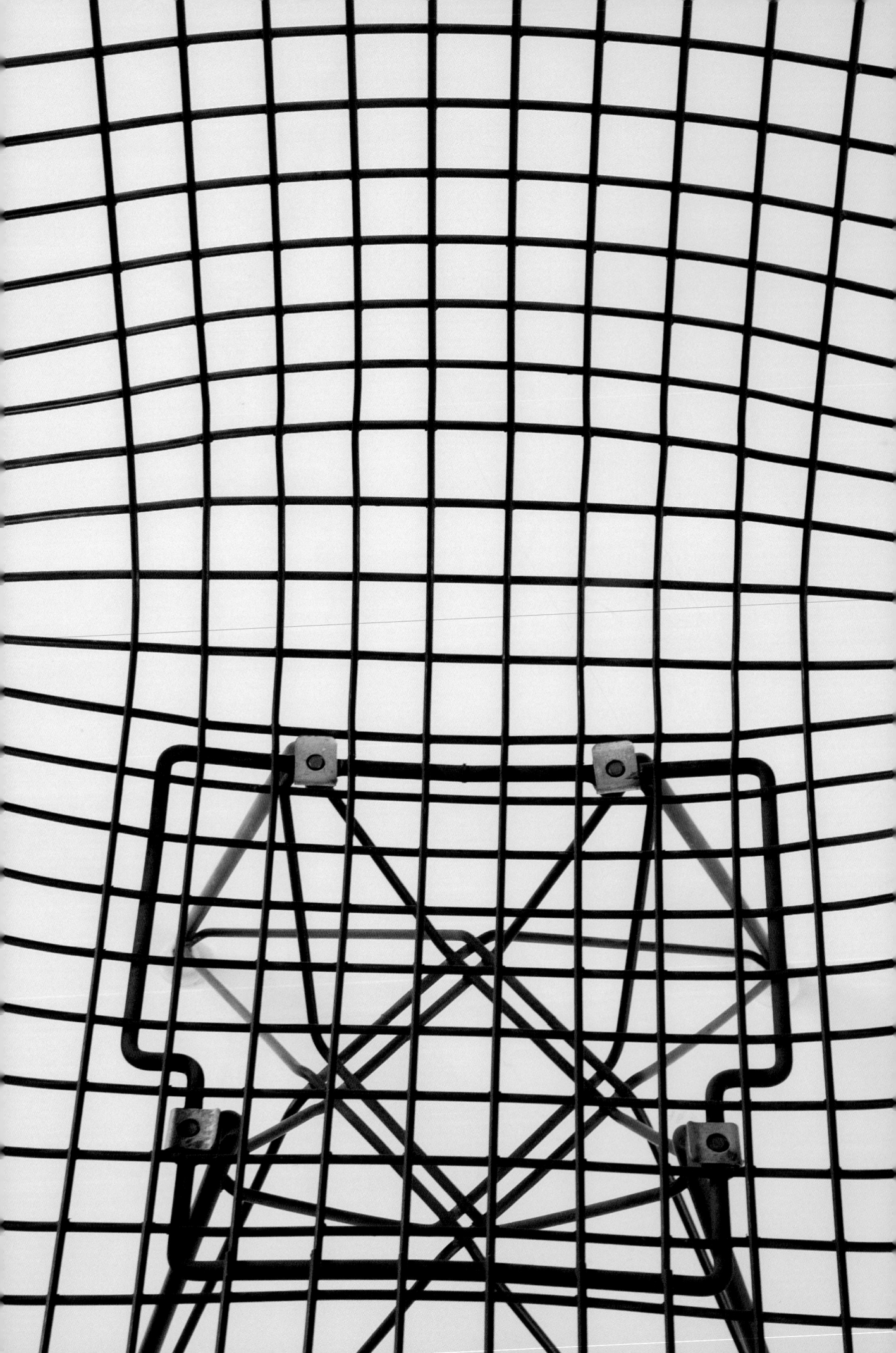

STEELWIRE

Upholstered wire chair—Eames' third milestone seating design—introduced the structural wire shell, trim mass-produced pad.

Welded steel shell formed in compound curves.

The wire base: a strong, lightweight space truss system.

The neatly tailored pad made easily removable by a snap-on perimeter wire.

From a 1953 Herman Miller advertisement created by the Eames Office

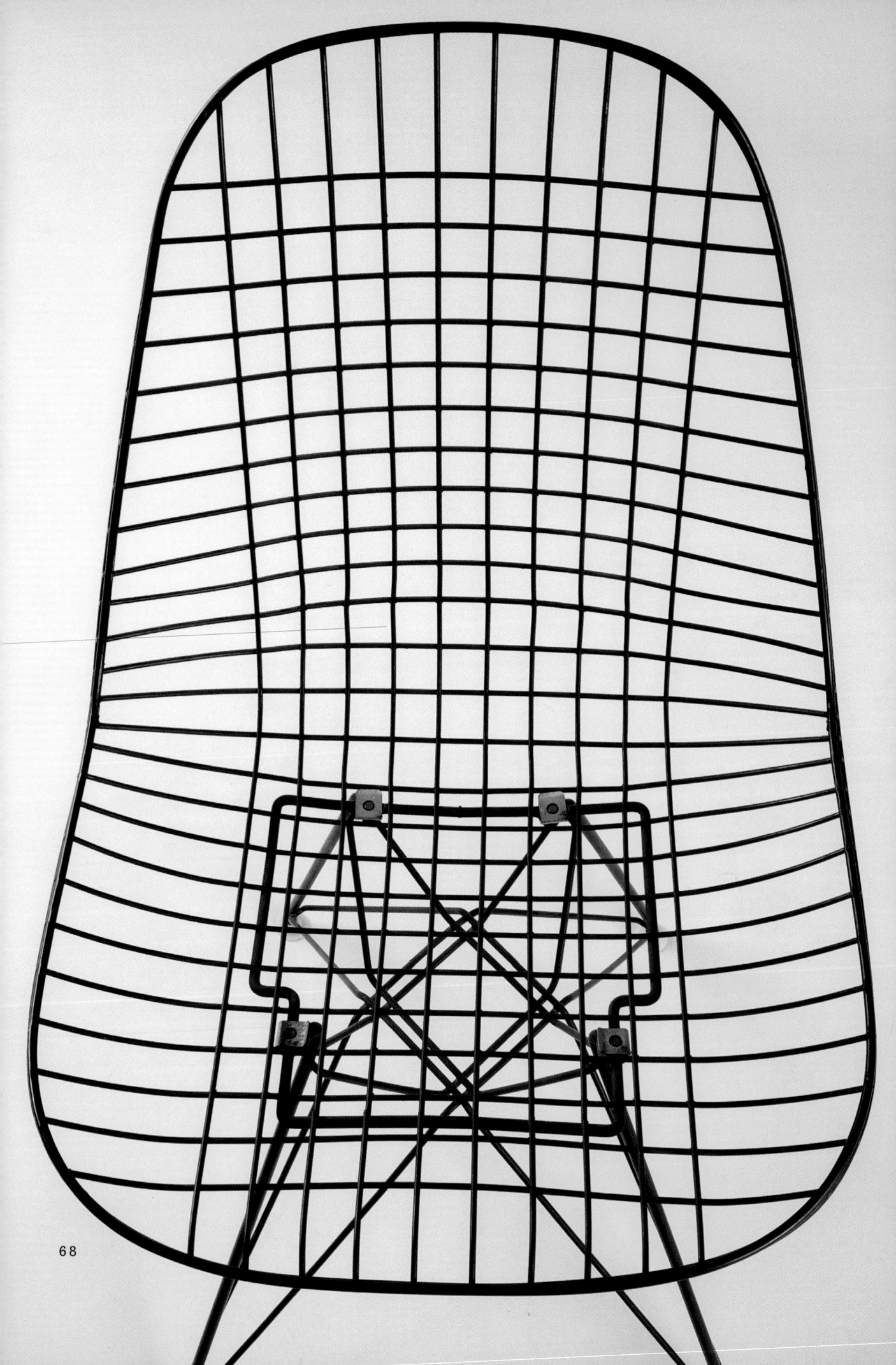

68

74

75

76

ALUMINUM

A major design by Charles Eames for the Herman Miller furniture collection, combines cast aluminum with other modern materials, in ingenious, purposeful lines. These new shapes, like fine sculptures, can be admired from any angle. They are impervious to weather, distinctly elegant indoors and easily portable for full time use.

From a 1958 Herman Miller advertisement, the first year the Eames aluminum chairs were introduced.

"The Indoor-Outdoor Group of Herman Miller chairs and tables brings a new airiness to residential settings, a freshness to hotel lobbies and reception rooms, to club lounges and dining areas. These distinctive shapes signal another important step in modern furniture design and maintenance ease."

From a 1958 Herman Miller brochure heralding the *The Indoor-Outdoor Group*, the name by which the Eames aluminum group chairs were first known.

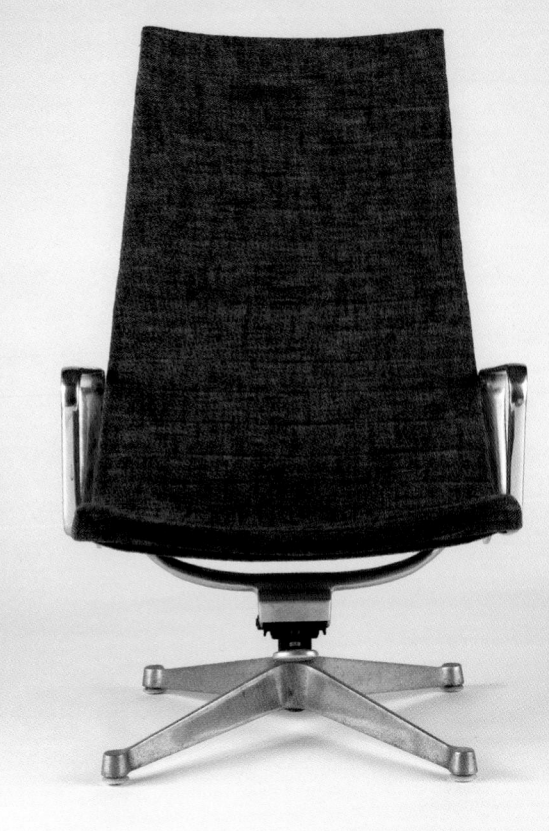

88

ALUMINUM

TABLES

"Herman Miller has long manufactured tables for a wide variety of uses.

Not only are Herman Miller tables purchased for their design integrity but also for their long-term value made possible by superior construction features: die-cast aluminum base for non-scuffing and easier maintenance, steel tube column for strength and rigidity, self-adjusting glides for tables without wobble, excellent variety of oiled veneers and plastic laminates, Eames vinyl edge, soft yet durable, to protect the table edge against any damage, die-cast aluminum spider, able to support the man who sits on the edge of the table."

From the Herman Miller Product File, 1970, "Tables."

96

100

SOFAS

"Charles Eames first sofa, for Herman Miller, incorporates all the qualities that distinguish his chairs: comfort, durability, light-weight, light scale; and it combines the comfort of a high back and foam rubber upholstery with a sturdy, slender frame.

It is covered with a choice of Herman Miller fabrics or Elastic Naugahyde in exclusive Herman Miller colors. Ships and stores in a flat carton. Ideal for homes, offices, reception areas; anywhere, where service, budget and pleasure are decisive considerations."

From the back of a 1954 postcard advertising the first Eames sofa, created by the Eames Office.

104

106

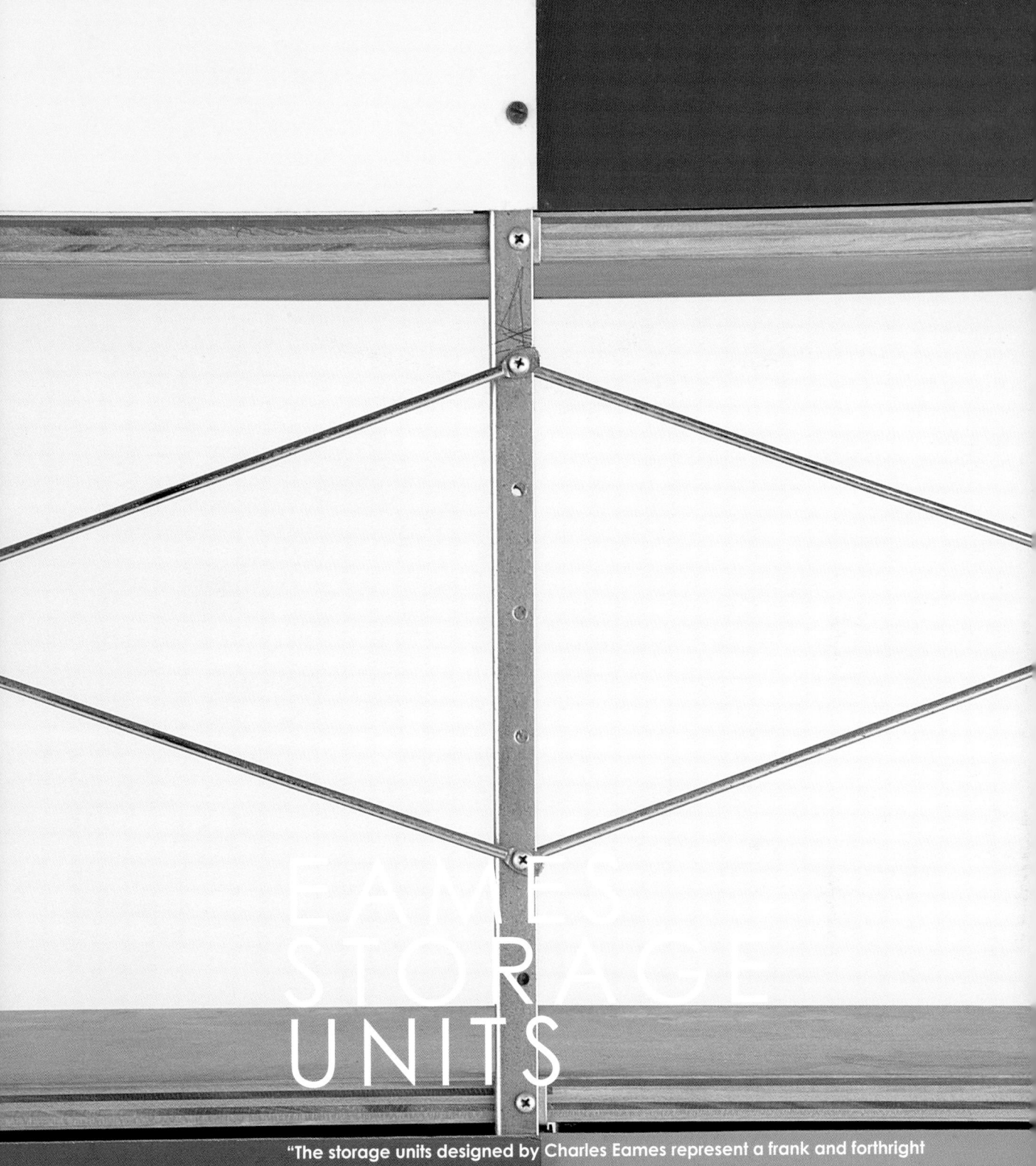

EAMES STORAGE UNITS

"The storage units designed by Charles Eames represent a frank and forthright answer to a permanent and basic furniture need: attractive, durable cabinets, cases and desks that are modestly priced. Plated steel uprights support plastic-coated plywood shelves and stain resistant wood or plastic coated tops. Crossed metal struts or lacquered masonite panels insure stability. The units come in two widths: 24" and 47" and in three heights: 20," 32 ½," and 59 ½." All are 16" deep. There are numerous arrangements including open shelves, sliding panel doors and drawers, in a variety of color combinations. In its entirety, it is a fluid comprehensive system that should answer most storage requirements."

From a 1951 Herman Miller brochure entitled ESU [Eames Storage Units]

eames soft pad group

eames soft pad group   herman miller inc

GRAPHIC DESIGN

Charles and Ray Eames, 1977 Medal Winners, American Institute of Graphic Arts.

The medal of AIGA—the most distinguished in the field—is awarded to individuals in recognition of their exceptional achievements, services or other contributions to the field of design and visual communication. The contribution may be in the practice of design, teaching, writing or leadership of the profession. The awards may honor designers posthumously.

Medals have been awarded since 1920 to individuals who have set standards of excellence over a lifetime of work or have made individual contributions to innovation within the practice of design.

Individuals who are honored may work in any country, but the contribution for which they are honored should have had a significant impact on the practice of graphic design in the United States.

OLLECTION—COLORS AND FINISHES

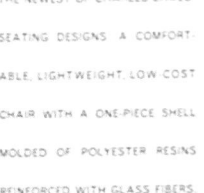

UPHOLSTERY

A-387 red · A-387 black · A-372 tweed · leather · raw umber · red

NAUGAHYDE

charcoal · blue

HARD PLASTIC

white · grey

white · yellow · blue · tan · grey

black · soft · red

greye · red · elephant hide grey · yellow

DESIGNED BY CHARLES EAMES

herman miller furniture company, zeeland michigan

MOLDED PLYWOOD CHAIRS

AMERICA'S MOST FAMOUS MODERN CHAIR. SEAT AND BACK OF MOLDED PLYWOOD. THE ELECTRONICALLY WELDED RUBBER SHOCK MOUNTS PERMIT A SLIGHT FLEX TO CONFORM WITH CHANGES IN POSITION. IN ITS VARIOUS HEIGHTS AND SIZES THIS CHAIR IS ADAPTED TO HOME, OFFICE, RESTAURANT AND STORE USE FOR DINING, LOUNGING OR WORK.

DCM · LCM · LCW

DESIGNED BY CHARLES EAMES

MOLDED PLASTIC SIDE C

THE NEWEST OF CHARLES EAMES SEATING DESIGNS, A COMFORTABLE, LIGHTWEIGHT, LOW-COST CHAIR WITH A ONE-PIECE SHELL MOLDED OF POLYESTER RESINS REINFORCED WITH GLASS FIBERS. FOR OFFICE, HOME AND INSTITUTIONAL USES, INDOORS OR OUT.

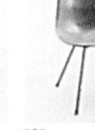

DSX · DSR · MSX

herman miller furniture company, zeeland

RED PLASTIC ARMCHAIRS

A TAILORED FOAM RUBBER PAD IS FITTED OVER THE MOLDED PLASTIC SHELL IN THESE NEW DESIGNS BY CHARLES EAMES. THE UPHOLSTERED PAD IS A SINGLE UNIT WHICH MAY BE REMOVED FOR EASY CLEANING. THESE CHAIRS ARE COMFORTABLE, LIGHTWEIGHT, COLORFUL SEATING SOLUTIONS FOR HOME, OFFICE OR COMMERCIAL INSTALLATIONS.

DAR-1 · DAT-1

RAR-1 · LAR-1

MOLDED PLASTIC ARMCHAIRS

THESE CHAIRS ARE MOLDED IN A HYDRAULIC PRESS, OF PLASTIC REINFORCED WITH GLASS FIBERS. THE MATERIAL AND THE METHOD ARE IDENTICAL WITH THE PROCESS USED TO MANUFACTURE AIRPLANE PARTS WHICH MUST ENDURE TREMENDOUS IMPACT. THEY ARE ADAPTED FOR USE RANGING FROM THE HOME TO OFFICES, RESTAURANTS, SCHOOLS, AND SHIPS.

DAX · DAR · DAT

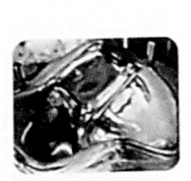

MAX · RAR · LAR

DESIGNED BY CHARLES EAMES

furniture company, zeeland michigan

herman miller furniture company, zeeland

PHOLSTERED WIRE CHAIRS

THE FORMED WIRE SHELL OF THESE CHAIRS IS WELDED INTO A SINGLE, LIGHTWEIGHT UNIT. THE DOUBLE PERIMETER WIRE FORMS A CONTINUOUS OPEN TRUSS FOR ADDED STRENGTH. THE VERSIONS SHOWN HERE HAVE TWO-PIECE UPHOLSTERED PADS WHICH ARE EASILY REMOVABLE FOR CLEANING. THE BASE STYLES ARE SUITABLE FOR DINING, READING AND LOUNGING.

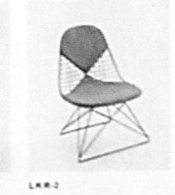

DKR-2

RKR-2 · LKR-2

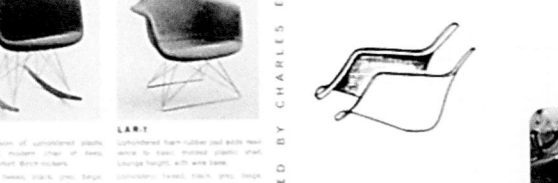

UPHOLSTERED WIRE CHAIRS

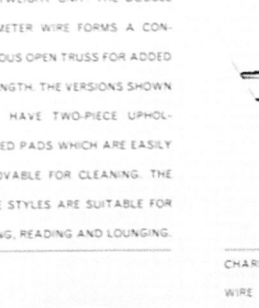

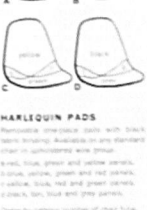

DKX-1 · DKR-1 · HARLEQUIN PADS

CHARLES EAMES' UPHOLSTERED WIRE CHAIR IS STILL ANOTHER INVENTIVE SOLUTION TO THE PROBLEM OF PRODUCING A LIGHTWEIGHT, COMFORTABLE CHAIR FOR A VARIETY OF PURPOSES. THE WELDED WIRE SHELL IS CAREFULLY

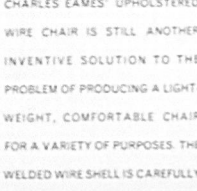

MKX-1 · RKR-1 · LKR-1

DESIGNED BY CHARLES EAMES

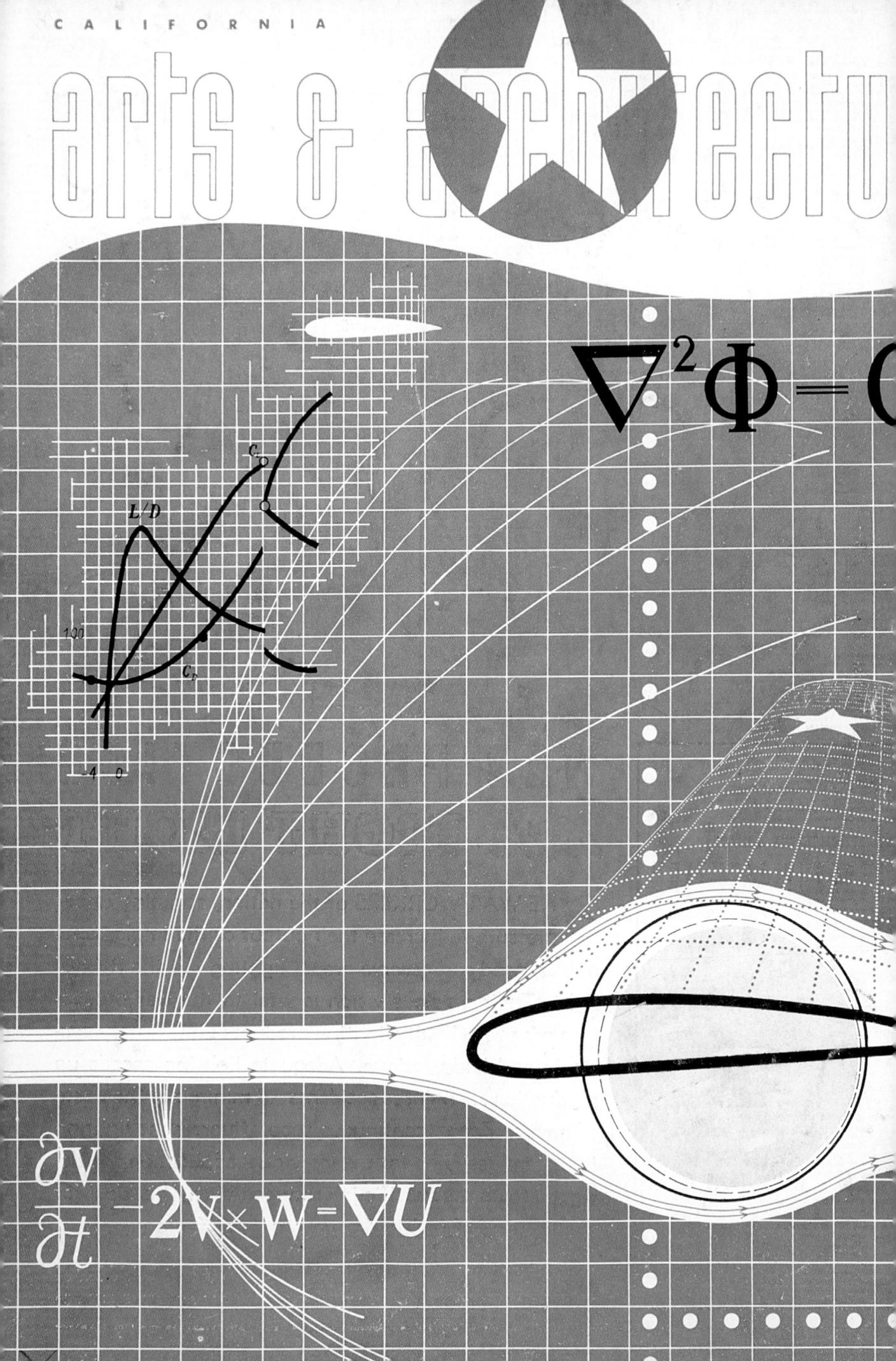

arts & architecture

SEPTEMBER 1946

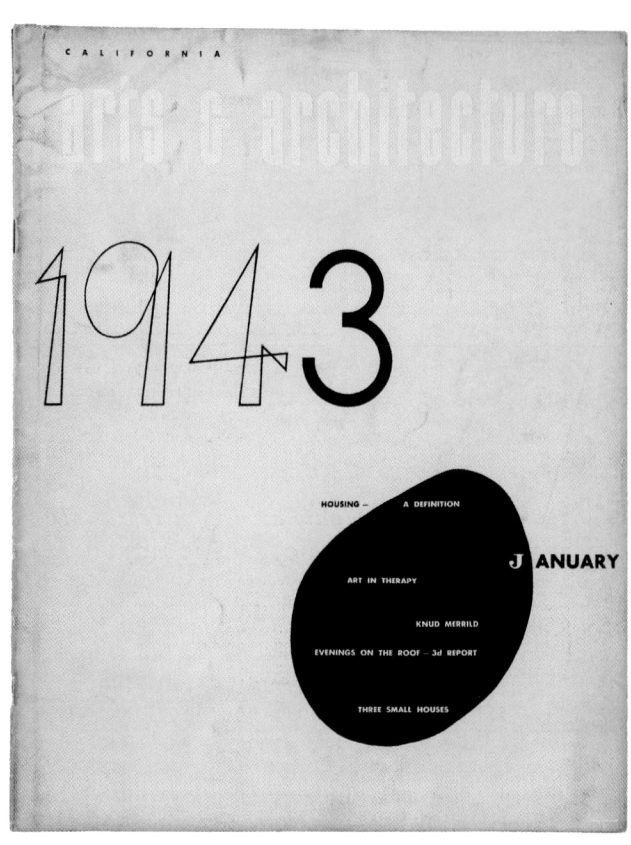

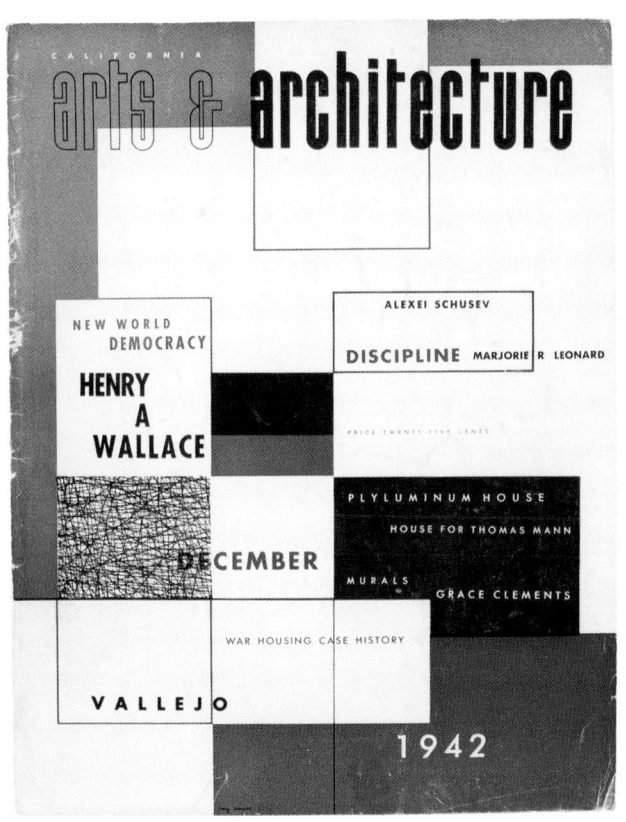

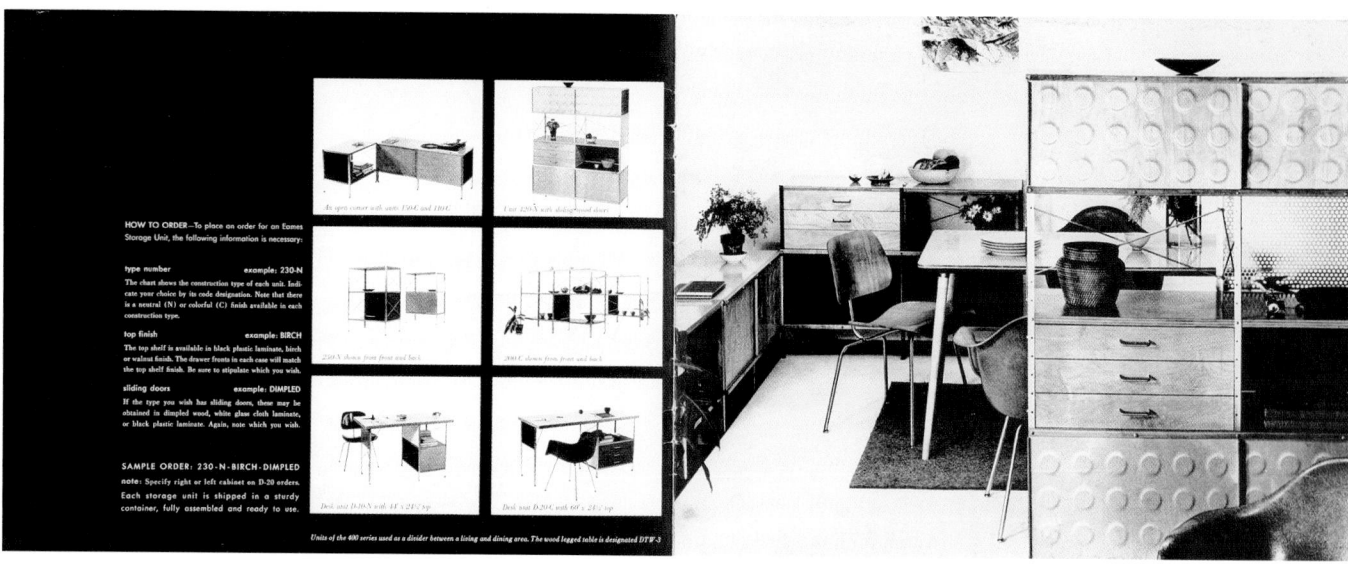

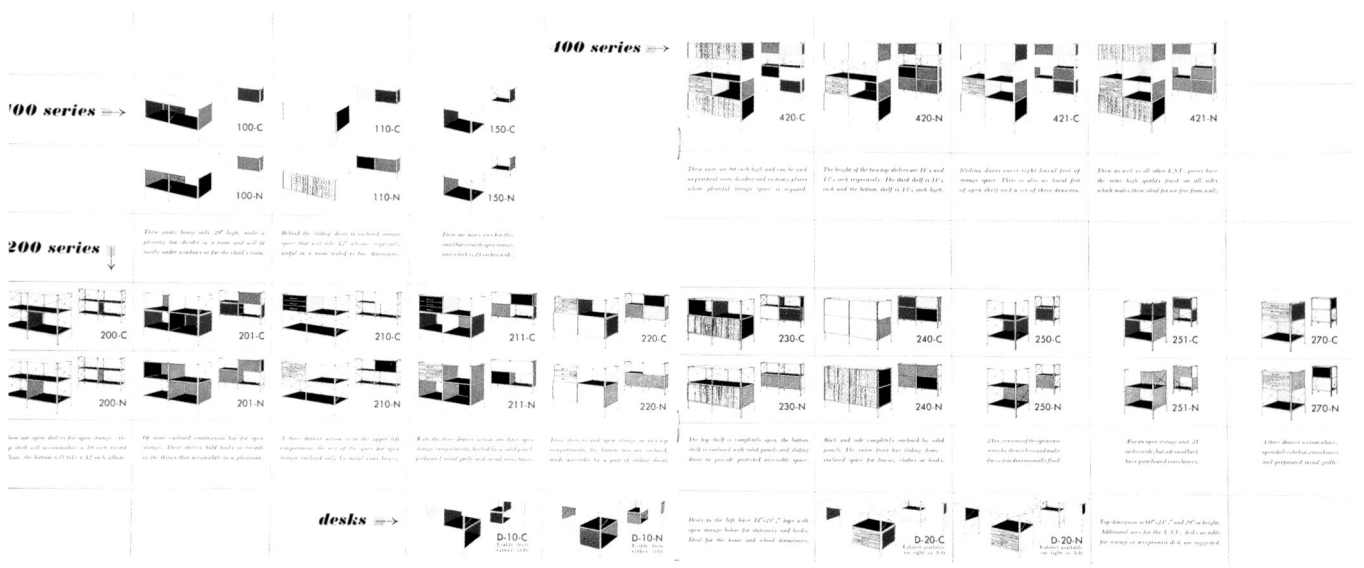

124

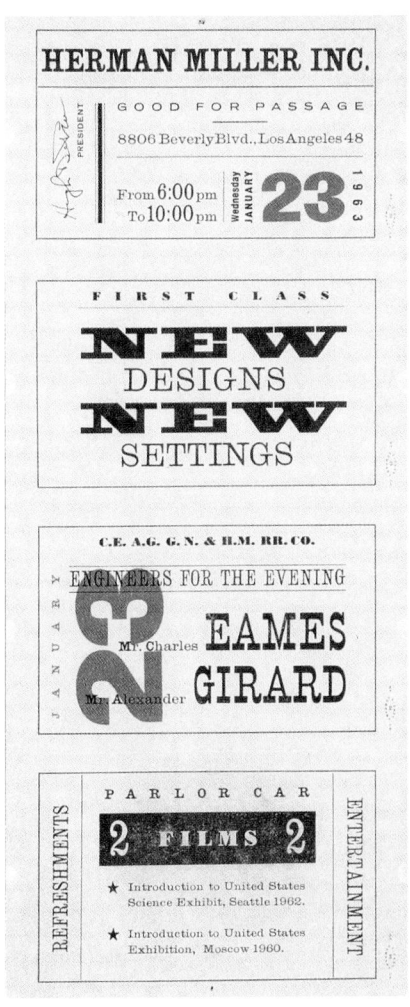

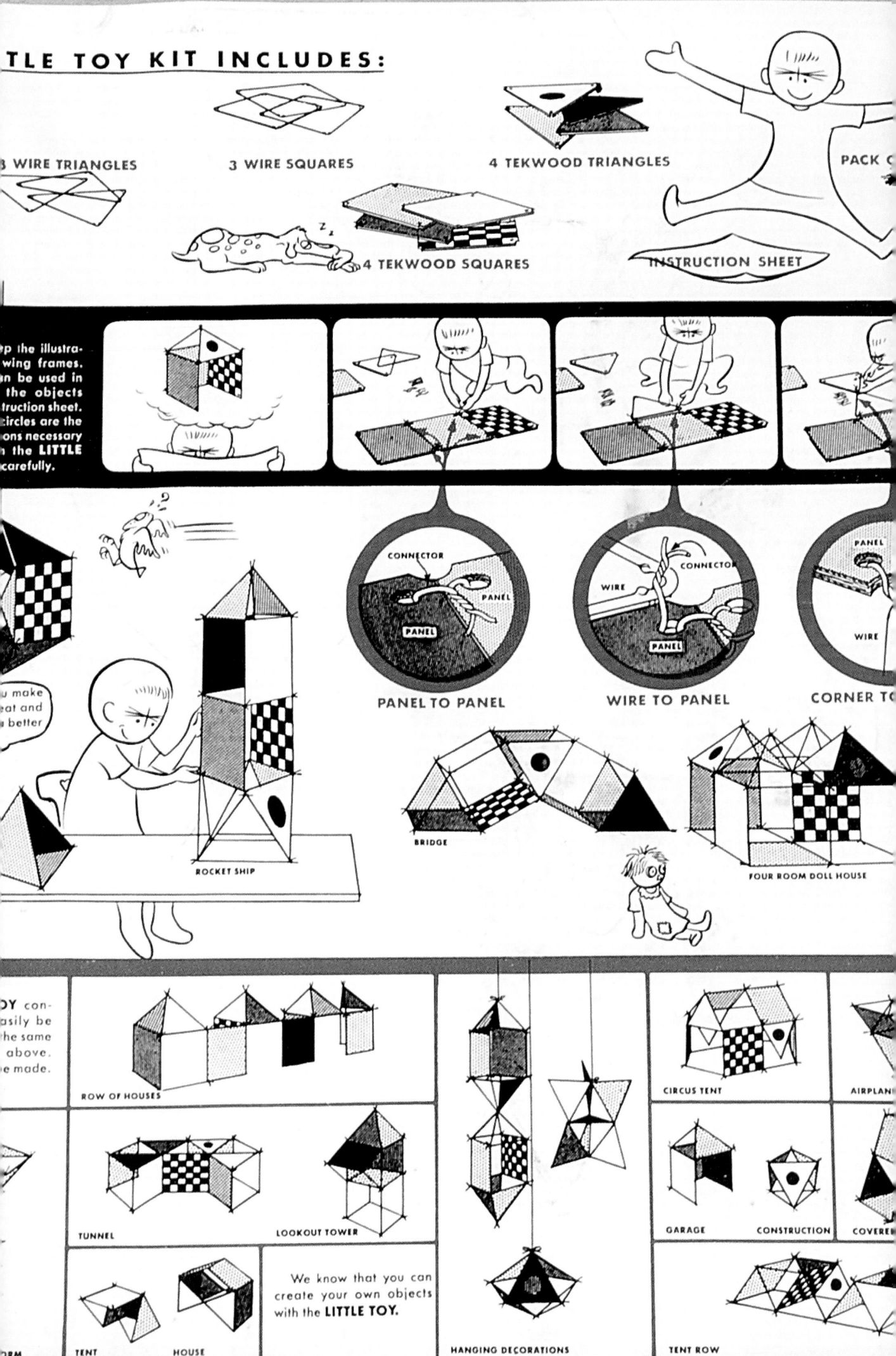

TLE TOY KIT INCLUDES:

3 WIRE TRIANGLES

3 WIRE SQUARES

4 TEKWOOD TRIANGLES

PACK

4 TEKWOOD SQUARES

INSTRUCTION SHEET

p the illustra-
wing frames.
n be used in
the objects
truction sheet.
circles are the
ons necessary
the **LITTLE**
carefully.

u make
eat and
better

CONNECTOR
PANEL
PANEL

PANEL TO PANEL

WIRE
CONNECTOR
PANEL

WIRE TO PANEL

PANEL
WIRE

CORNER TO

ROCKET SHIP

BRIDGE

FOUR ROOM DOLL HOUSE

OY con-
asily be
he same
above.
e made.

ROW OF HOUSES

CIRCUS TENT

AIRPLAN

TUNNEL

LOOKOUT TOWER

GARAGE

CONSTRUCTION

COVERE

RM

TENT

HOUSE

We know that you can
create your own objects
with the **LITTLE TOY.**

HANGING DECORATIONS

TENT ROW

TOYS

"Two decks of cards, 108 different designs reproduced with patterns and with pictures gathered from sources all over the globe. With them you can make buildings, bridges, cities–a miniature world in your own home."

Pattern Deck: A colorful collection of 54 cards, each one different, bearing the patterns and the textures of book papers, fabrics, cutouts and wrappings from England, France, China, Japan, Germany, Switzerland and America.

Picture Deck: Familiar and nostalgic objects from the animal, mineral and vegetable kingdoms: 54 photographs of things old and new— a collection rich in color and form to delight adults and children everywhere.

From the original 1953 instruction sheet for the House of Cards, created by the Eames Office.

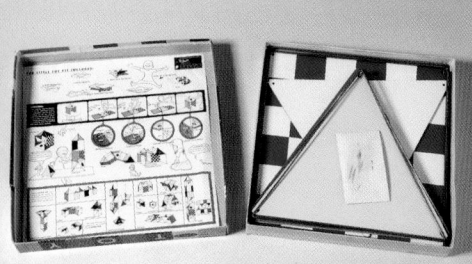

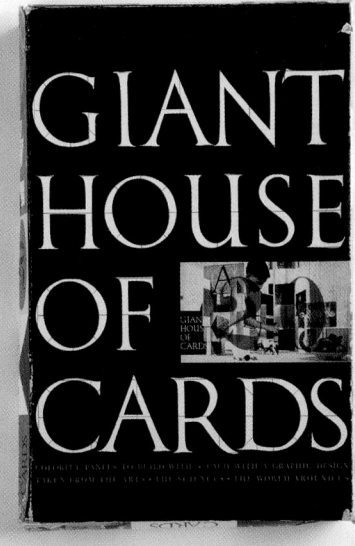

GIANT
HOUSE
OF
CARDS

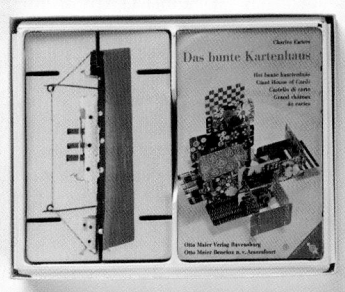

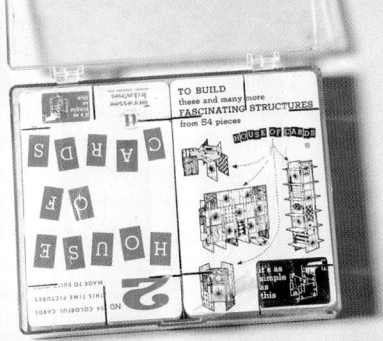

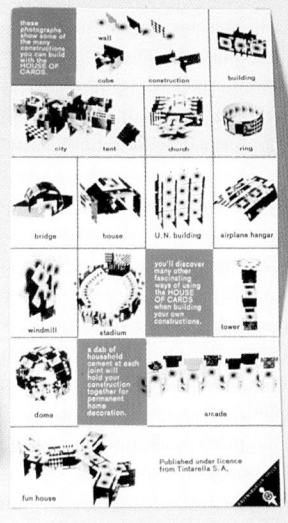

In these captions you can find the model number or name by which an Eames design was known in the Eames Office and by their authorized manufacturer, and the date of production of the particular example shown. Almost all the pieces in the JF Chen Eames Collection were manufactured by Herman Miller, Inc., and those few exceptions have their manufacturers listed in [brackets].

Materials are only noted where a finish or material is a custom finish.* There are many rare examples in this collection, but rarity was often a function of production and demand, not of special finishes. Some of the most rare Eames items are standard production models that weren't produced very long, because the Eames Office and their manufacturing partner, Herman Miller, were and remain acutely sensitive to feedback from the public, and from their own observations of their designs in use over time.

The term custom finish may mislead one to a conclusion that a custom finish is somehow better or more desirable. In fact, all Eames designs were and are custom made, because that is how quality American manufacturer Herman Miller did and does their business. If you were to walk into the Herman Miller showroom on Beverly Boulevard in 1965 and order an Eames molded plastic rocking chair, you would be asked to specify the color of plastic, and the type of finish you wanted on the rod base. Then you would invited to come back in three to six weeks to pick up your rocking chair. Thus, all of the Eames designs in this collection are signed, custom, made-to-order-for-one-particular-buyer pieces.

1: 650 Table, 1957.

10, 12, 13: Relaxing chair, 1941, 1st place winner, MOMA Organic Design competition, designed by Charles Eames & Eero Saarinen. This example -with its original Marli Ehrlman weave, a textile which also won first place in the competition- was exhibited at MOMA. Metal supports added later. [Heywood-Wakefield.]

14, 15: Kleinhans chair, 1939, designed by Charles Eames & Eero Saarinen for the Kleinhans Music Hall. The building was designed by Eliel Saarinen with his son, Eero Saarinen and "was recognized as one of the greatest concert halls ever built in the United States." It was declared a National Historic Landmark in 1989. [Custom made for Kleinhans Music Hall]

16, 17, 18, 19: Organic Design Case Goods, 1941, designed by Charles Eames & Eero Saarinen, who won first place in the category of case goods with these designs. [Red Lion]

20: Details, two DCMs.

22, 23: Details, two DCMS with custom leather upholstery.

24, 25: Eight DCMS, with custom leather upholstery.t

26: CTM, 1947, [Evans].

27: CTW, 1950.

28: Clockwise from top left: CTW, 1950; CTM, 1954; CTM, 1947 [Evans].

29: Clockwise from top left: CTW, 1950; CTM, 1954; CTM, 1947 [Evans]; CTM, 1952.

30, 31: FSW 10, 1950.

32, 33: DCM, 1952, original leather upholstery.

34, 35: DCW, 1950, original leather upholstery.

36: Clockwise from top left: DCM, 1959; DCM 1952; LCW-1 with original custom upholstery 1949; LCM, 1954.

37: Clockwise from top left: DCW, 1946 [Evans]; DCW, 1947 [Evans]; DCM, 1951; DCM, 1963.

38: Child's stool/table, 1945, [Evans].

39, 40: Childs chair, 1945, [Evans].

41: Clockwise from top left: DCM, 1963, DCW, 1950, DCM, 1970, custom wenge wood and eggplant colored finish on the metal, DCM, 1953.

42: Left to right: DSX-1, 1953; DSR-1, 1970.

43: Left to right: PSCC-4, 1962, DSS, 1952.

44: Detail, underside, molded plastic chair.

46: Clockwise from top left: DAT-1, 1953, DAT-1, 1958, RAR-1, 1983, DAX-1, 1976.

47: Clockwise from top left: DAX-1, 1954, PAC-1, 1979, LAR, 1954, PAW, 1952.

48: Clockwise from top left: RAR-1, 1983, RAR-1, 1979, RKR-1, 1960, RKR-1, 1951.

49: RAR, 1950.

50: RAR, 1950.

51: RXR, 1949, model for a design not produced.

52: DAX-1, 1954.

53: DAX-1, 1976.

54: Left to right: DSR-1, 1979; PSCA-36, 1970.

55: PSCA, 1972.

56, 57: DSX-1, 1957.

58, 59: DSR-1, 1970, showroom floor set of four, from a former Herman Miller salesman.

60: From left to right: Loose Cushion Armchair, 1971, DAX-99, 1966.

61: From left to right: EC 228, 1972; PSCC-4, 1962.

62, 63: La Chaise, 1998, Vitra (formerly in the collection of Tim Burton).

64: PAC-1, 1971, matched set of four.

65: Clockwise from top left: LAX, 1951; Drafting chair 622TS-1, 1959; DSS, 1957; EC 228, 1972.

66, 68: DKR, detail.

69, 70, 71: DKX-1, 1954, original Harlequin upholstery.

72: Left to right: DKR-1, 1951; DKW-2, 1951.

71: Left to right: LKR-2, 1969; RKR-2, 1953.

74: DKR-1, 1954, original Harlequin upholstery.

75: DKR-1, 1952.

76: Clockwise from top left: PKC-1, 1955; DKW-1, 1952; PKC-1, 1958; PKCC-1, 1959.

77: PKC-1, 1959, matched pair.

78: PKCC-2, 1959

70: PKC-1, 1959, matched pair.

80, 81: DKX-1, 1957, matched set of four.

82: Detail, Eames aluminum group chair.

84: Detail, ES 102.

85: Details, Eames aluminum group chairs.

86: 685, Eames aluminum group ottoman, 1962.

87: 685, Eames aluminum group ottoman, 1962, with custom fitted top.

88: Clockwise from top left: 680, with original Saran upholstery, 1958, 684, 1960, 686 S, 1965, 686 S, 1965, EA 107 Aluminum Group Swivel Arm Chair, 1969, 684 Reclining chair with pillow and arms, 1959.

89: Clockwise from top left: ES 102, 1968; 675 Time-Life Lobby Chair, 1960; EA 115 Aluminum Group Lounge Arm Chair, 1972; 684 Reclining Chair with Pillow and Arms, 1959.

90, 91, 92, 93: Eames Chaise, 1970

94: Top to bottom: IT-10 (Incidental Table), 1952, IT-1 (Incidental Table), 1952.

96: ET 142, Eames Rectangular Segmented Base Conference Table, 1972, custom original top, CTW-1, 1952, DTW-50, 1952.

98, 99: Eames Oval Segmented Base Conference Table, 1972.

98: Clockwise from top left: IT-10 (Incidental Table), 1952, IT-1 (Incidental Table), 1952, LTR, 1949, custom original Birdseye Maple top, 650 Table, 1957.

101: From top to bottom: 690 Dining table MODEL, 1957. 690 Dining table, custom original black top.

102, 103: Detail, S-73, Compact sofa, 1960.

104: S-73, Eames Compact Sofa, 1960, custom original upholstery.

105: 3473 Sofa, 1965.

106: ESU 440-C, 1953.

107: Detail, ESU 425-C, 1953.

108: ESU 425_C, 1953.

109: ESU 226-N, 1953.

110: From top to bottom: ESU D-10-N, 1951,; ESU D-30-C, 1953; ESU D-20-C, 1951

111: From top to bottom: ESU D-30-C, 1953; ESU D-10-N, 1951; ESU D-20-C, 1951.

112: Eames soft pad group poster, 1969.

114: UCLA "Connections: The Work of Charles and Ray Eames" exhibition poster, 1976.

115: Clockwise from top left: "The Work of Charles and Ray Eames," Design Museum exhibition poster, 1999; "The Gifted Eye of Charles Eames," Eames Office exhibition poster, 2008; "Mathematica" Boston Museum of Science poster, 1961.

116: Herman Miller screenprint on canvas of a 1961 Don Ervin for George Nelson & Associates design. From a numbered edition of 500.

117: "Chairs: Charles Eames For the Herman Miller Furniture Company" poster, 1953.

118: Clockwise from left: "Eames Design," Tokyo Museum poster, 2001; "Le Monde De Franklin & Jefferson," Eames Office exhibition poster, 1976.

119: From left to right: "The Work of Charles and Ray Eames/A Legacy of Invention," Meguro Museum of Art poster, 2005; "Eames Design," Tokyo Metropolitan Art Museum, 2002.

120: Arts & Architecture, cover by Ray Eames, November 1942.

121: Arts & Architecture, cover by Herbert Matter, September 1946.

122: Clockwise from top left: Arts & Architecture, cover by Ray Eames, May 1942; Arts & Architecture, cover by Ray Eames, January 1943; Arts & Architecture, cover by Ray Eames, September 1943; Arts & Architecture, cover by Ray Eames, August 1944.

123: Clockwise from top left: Arts & Architecture, cover by Ray Eames, February 1943; Arts & Architecture, cover by Ray Eames, April 1942; Arts & Architecture, cover by Ray Eames. September 1942; Arts & Architecture, cover by Ray Eames, December 1942.

124: "Eames Storage Units," Eames Office design for Herman Miller, 1951.

125: Herman Miller showroom announcements, Eames Office design for Herman Miller, 1961

126: The Little Toy, original insert, 1952. [Tigrett]

128: Clockwise from top left: The Little Toy, 1952 [Tigrett]; House of Cards, detail, 1960 [Ravensburg]; House of Cards, detail, 1960 [Ravensburg]; Giant House of Cards, 1953 [Tigrett]; The Little Toy, 1952 [Tigrett]; House of Cards, Picture Deck and Pattern Deck, 1952, [Summit/Tigrett]; Giant House of Cards, 1961 [Ravensburg]

128: Clockwise from top left: House of Cards detail [Ravensburg]; Giant House of Cards, 1953 [Tigrett]; Giant House of Cards, 1953 [Tigrett]; House of Cards, 1960 [Ravensburg]; House of Cards Two Deck Pack, 1964 (?) [Creative Playthings]

130: Eames Chair and Ottoman by Cheryl Ekstrom, 2007. Stainless steel full scale sculpture of the Eames lounge chair and ottoman, with exclusive permission from the Eames Office. 5 of a limited edition of 5."

134: From left to right: LCW, 1953; DKR, 1960; "La Fonda" Arm chair, 1964; RAR, 1959.

136: Eames Office Bearbrick, 2007.

*I use the word "original" with regard to finish or upholstery only where it is clear that the finish or upholstery was applied by Herman Miller. In some instances it is difficult to know, so I have taken a conservative approach.

134

ACKNOWLEDGMENTS

At the time of writing this, an Eames show is being prepared in conjunction with The Getty's Pacific Standard Time initiative, and it is coming out beautifully. The show, "Collecting Eames: The JF Chen Collection" is being held at Exhibit C and comprises my entire collection of 425 Eames pieces. The entire scope and production of this show is being achieved with enormous support and assistance from the Eames Office, Eames Demetrios and Daniel Ostroff—all to whom we are enormously indebted for their knowledge, for loaning their treasured graphic elements and for the comprehensive website eamesdesigns.com, in which my entire collection and captions are stored.

I extend my heartfelt gratitude to my friend Andy Hackman, who has supported me all of the way and without even realizing it, has been both an emotional support and a professional mentor, providing invaluable knowledge and insight, as well as immense resources.

I would like to thank Bryan Van Gorder and Max Padilla whose firm BVGPR, has helped to reach out to numerous institutions and periodicals. And Victoria Lam whose ingenious design of the book has taken it to a higher level—one that extends far beyond the average, good-looking coffee table book.

I would also like to thank the entire staff at JF Chen who has been working diligently to clear out Exhibit C in preparation for the show and arranging all the pieces for it. To the people of Maharam who answered all of my requests for use of their precious fabrics, and Clare Graham and Robert Breen who are designing the show in an impossibly tight time schedule, thank you. Much appreciation to artist and friend Cheryl Ekstrom, who has generously loaned to our exhibition her limited edition, all steel, full scale replica of the Eames 670 and 671 lounge chair and ottoman. It is an honor to display her work with our collection.

I extend my gratitude and appreciation to Wendy Kaplan and Bobbye Tigerman of LACMA who inspired me to emulate and complement their show. And to 1st Dibs, Herman Miller and Nike who trusted in JF Chen and sponsored us in creating a world-class show.

And to my dear friend Daniel Ostroff, who should be mentioned independently as an extremely enthusiastic, all things Eames, insightful, experienced person. His job as "Vintage Eames" at the Eames Office has already contributed a bundle in reaching out to the public. I bought his initial collection and he has helped to expand it into the extraordinary collection it is today in terms of technology, history and philosophy of all things Eames. Thank you Daniel!

A million thanks to our musical friends at Dublab, especially Carlos Nino and Mark "Frosty" McNeill, who provide us with beautiful music at every one of our events. Once again, I am relying on them for this one.

Thank you to The Tropics, Inc. and Ryan Hroziencik for always contributing such beautiful plants to complement our exhibits and events.

And last, but certainly not least, I must thank my wife, Margaret, for her understanding, support and for managing the most difficult task of all—the budget-less budget. And to my two daughters, Bianca and Fiona, who have worked incessantly to make all of this happen within the most impossible deadline. Thank you for enduring my neurotic tendencies! I am grateful to have such a talented and supportive family.

—Joel Chen

First published in 2011 by
JF Chen
941 North Highland Avenue
Los Angeles, CA 90038
www.jfchen.com

© 2011 by JF Chen
ISBN 978-0-615-54635-3

Book published in conjunction with the exhibition
COLLECTING EAMES: THE JF CHEN COLLECTION
& is a participating gallery of the Getty's Pacific Standard Time: ART IN LA 1945-1980
Curator: Daniel Ostroff
Exhibition Design: Clare Graham and Bob Breen
The exhibit was generously sponsored by Herman Miller, 1st Dibs, and Nike.
JF Chen Staff: Mynor Cordon, Miguel Garcia, Leonel Magana, Roger Villamil
Gabrielle Burik, Paige Reynolds, Wendy Rowlett, Justine Wu

Book Concept: Joel Chen and Daniel Ostroff
Book Design: Victoria Lam
Text: Daniel Ostroff
Photography: Grant Taylor
Printer: Heinz Weber Inc., Los Angeles